This book is dedicated to my nephews,

Judah & Keith, Jr.

To all the young princes reading this book.

And to my support system! You know who you are!

Phil 4:13

Hi, my name is Isaiah.

I am six years old and
I am in the first grade.

Because of COVID my parents have to go to work.

So I need to pack my
backpack for school.

They both want to make sure that I am really safe.

So they put everything I
will need on the table.

I need to count all of
these items one by one.

Then we will place it
all in my backpack.
Will you help me?

$$0 + 1 = 1$$

One Ruler

1 + 1 = 2

Two Hand Sanitizers

1 + 2 = 3

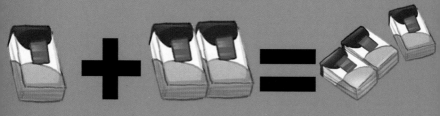

Three Pocket
Tissues

1 + 3 = 4

Four Notebooks

$$1 + 4 = 5$$

Five Erasers

$1 + 5 = 6$

Six Colored Pencils

$$1 + 6 = 7$$

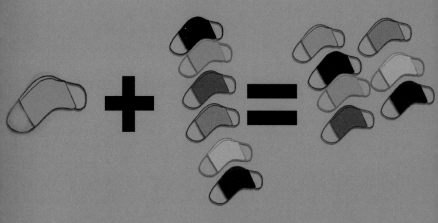

Seven Face Masks

$1 + 7 = 8$

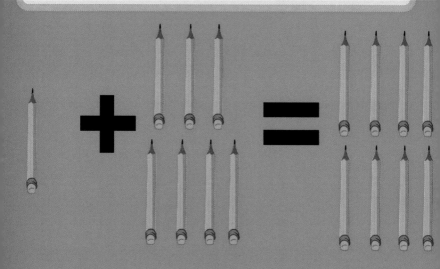

Eight Pencils

1 + 8 = 9

Nine Markers

1 + 9 = 10

Ten Crayons

We did it! We added
each group by ones!

Now I am all packed
up and ready to go.

Thank you for your help.

Time to get on my school bus. Goodbye for now.

Made in the USA
Coppell, TX
25 February 2021